21ST CENTUI
SMASH HITS

WISE PUBLICATIONS
part of The Music Sales Group
London / New York / Paris / Sydney / Copenhagen / Berlin / Madrid / Tokyo

Published by
Wise Publications
14-15 Berners Street, London W1T 3LJ, UK.

Exclusive Distributors:
Music Sales Limited
Distribution Centre, Newmarket Road,
Bury St Edmunds, Suffolk IP33 3YB, UK.

Music Sales Pty Limited
120 Rothschild Avenue, Rosebery
NSW 2018, Australia.

Order No. AM92362
ISBN 0-7119-4438-5

This book © Copyright 2006 Wise Publications,
a division of Music Sales Limited.

Music arranged by Derek Jones and Jack Long.
Music processed by Paul Ewers Music Design.
Cover design by Ruth Keating.

Printed in the EU.

www.musicsales.com

Your guarantee of quality:
As publishers, we strive to produce every book
to the highest commercial standards.
The book has been carefully designed to
minimise awkward page turns and to make
playing from it a real pleasure.
Particular care has been given to specifying
acid-free, neutral-sized paper made from pulps
which have not been elemental chlorine bleached.
This pulp is from farmed sustainable forests
and was produced with special regard for the environment.
Throughout, the printing and binding have
been planned to ensure a sturdy, attractive
publication which should give years of enjoyment.
If your copy fails to meet our high standards,
please inform us and we will gladly replace it.

Previously published as *The Biggest Songs Of 2002* AM975898
& *Big Book Of Smash Hits 2003* AM977515

PART 1

CONTENTS

ALL THE THINGS SHE SAID

Words & Music by Sergei Galoyan, Trevor Horn, Martin Kierszenbaum, Elena Kiper & Valerij Polienko

All the things she said, all the things she said, run - ning through my
head, run - ning through my head, all the things she said. This is not e - nough.__

I'm in

se - ri - ous shit, I feel to - tal - ly lost,__ if I'm ask - ing for help__ it's on - ly be - cause__

be - ing with you_ has op - ened my eyes. Could I ev - er be - lieve such a per - fect sur - prise? I keep

ask - ing my - self, won - der - ing how._ I keep clos - ing my eyes, but I can't block you out._ Wan - na

fly to a place_ where it's just you and me,_ no - bo - dy else,_ so we can be free,_

(no - bo - dy else,_ so we can be free.)_ All the things she said, all the things she said, run - ning through my

2. And I'm all mixed up feel-ing corn-ered and rushed. They

say it's my fault, but I want her so much, wan-na fly her a-way where the sun and the rain_ come in

over my face, wash a-way all the shame. When they stop and stare, don't wor-ry me_ 'cause I'm

feel-ing for her____ what she's feel-ing for me.____ I can

try to pre-tend, I can try to for-get,_ but it's driv-ing me mad,_ go-ing out of my

head._____ All the things she said, all the things she said, run-ning through my

Mother, look-ing at me, tell me what do you see? Yes, I lost my mind.__
Dad-dy, look-ing at me, will I ev-er be free? Have I crossed the line?__

D.S. al Coda

Coda

All the things she said, all the things she said, all the things she

said. All the things she said, all the things she said, all the things she said.

BEAUTIFUL

Words & Music by Linda Perry

wonderful, then suddenly it's hard to breathe.
-lirious, so consumed in all your doom.

Now and then I get insecure from all the pain, I'm so a-
Trying hard to fill the emptiness, the pieces gone, left the puzzle

-shamed.
undone, is that the way it is? 'Cause you are beautiful, no
'Cause we are beautiful, no

I am beautiful, no

matter what they say. Words can't bring me down.
matter what they say. Words can't bring you down.
matter what they say. Yes words won't bring us down.

2.

E♭ 6fr

No mat - ter what we do, _____ no mat - ter what we say, _____

E♭7/D♭ 4fr

Cm 3fr

we're the song in - side the tune, _____ full of beau - ti - ful mis - takes. _____

B

E♭ 6fr

And ev - 'ry - where we go, _____ the sun will al - ways shine, _____

E♭7/D♭ 4fr

Cm 3fr

D.S. al Coda

but to - mor - row we might a - wake, _____ on the oth - er side. _____

B

BE MINE

Words & Music by David Gray & Craig McClune

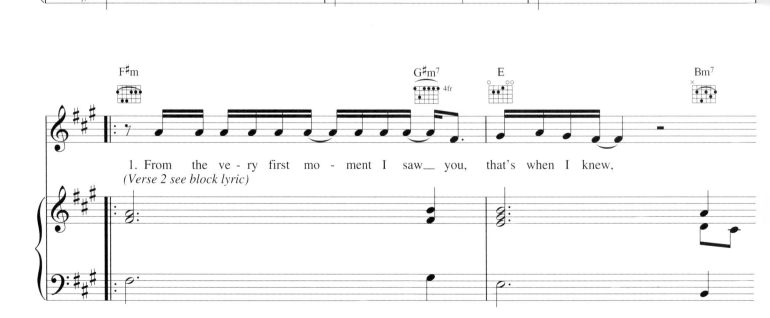

1. From the ve-ry first mo-ment I saw__ you, that's when I knew,
(Verse 2 see block lyric)

Jump - in' Je - sus, Ho - ly cow, what's the dif - ference a - ny - how,

ba - by till your heart be - longs to me.

(Vocal ad lib.)

(Bo - dy's on fire, my bo - dy's on fire. My bo - dy's on fire, my bo - dy's on fire. My

bo - dy's on fire and I'm los - ing my sa - ni - ty.) Be mine, be mine.

Verse 2:

If I had some influence girl
With the powers that be
I'd have them fire that arrow at you
Like they fired it right t me
And maybe when you're heart and soul are burning
You might see
That everytime I'm talking with you
It's always over too soon
That everyday feels so incomplete
Till you walk into the room
Say the word now girl
I'll jump that moon.

Come on baby it's OK
Rainy, shiny, night or day
There's nothing in the way now
Don't you see, be mine, be mine
Winter, summer, day or night
Centigrade or fahrenheit
Baby till you're heart belongs to me
Be mine, be mine.

BORN TO TRY

Words & Music by Delta Goodrem & Audius Mtawarira

1. Do-ing ev-'ry-thing that I___ be-lieve
2. No point in talk-ing what___ should have___

___ in
___ been

go-ing by the rules___ that I've___ been taught.___
and re-gret-ting the___ things that___ went on.___

More un-der-stand-ing of what's___ a-round me___
Life's full of mis-takes, des-ti-nies and___ fates.___

and pro-tect-ed____ from the walls____ of love.
Re-move the clouds, look at the big - ger pic - ture.

All that____ you see____

is me.

And all I tru-ly be-lieve____ that I was born to try,____

I've learned to love,_____ be un-der-stand-

-ing and be-lieve in life._____ But you got-ta make choi-

- ces, be wrong or right.____ Some - times you got -

- ta sa - cri - fice_ the things_ you like.____ But I was born to try.____

1. ____ ____

2. All that____ you see____

____ is me.____ And all I tru - ly be - lieve____ that I was born to try_

DON'T WORRY

Words & Music by D. Hastings, Natalie Appleton & Craigie Dodds

(In the hea - vens___ a - bove.)___

1. I just need - ed you___ to com - fort me,___

and I have tried___ to make it right.___

And I don't know_ that I_____ feel so sure,___
2. And all I want - ed was to stand a - lone,___ so is there

Don't wor - ry 'cause I'll al - ways be there_____ for you._

In the hea - vens_____ a - bove._

Don't wor - ry 'cause I'll al - ways be there_____ for you._

1.

Al - ways be there.

Al - ways be there.__
(Bro - ken man.)__

(Vocal ad lib.)

Yeah,__ yeah.____

CLOCKS

Words & Music by Guy Berryman, Jon Buckland, Will Champion & Chris Martin

1. The lights go out and I can't be saved, tides that I tried to
(Verse 2 see block lyric)

Verse 2:
Confusion that never stops
The closing walls and the ticking clocks
Gonna come back and take you home
I could not stop that you now know, singing:
Come out upon my seas
Cursed missed opportunities
Am I a part of the cure?
Or I am a part of the disease, singing:

You are *etc.*

COME UNDONE

Words & Music by Robbie Williams, Boots Ottestad, Ashley Hamilton & Daniel Pierre

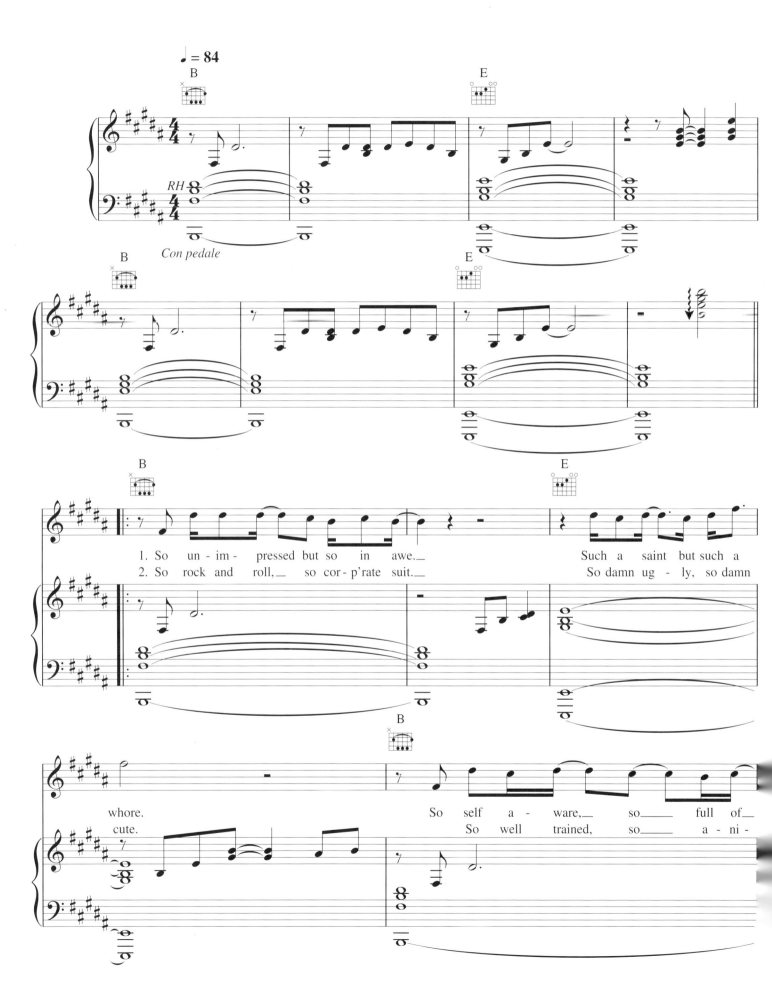

1. So un-im-pressed but so in awe._ Such a saint but such a whore.

2. So rock and roll,_ so cor-p'rate suit._ So damn ug-ly, so damn cute.

So self a-ware,_ so_ full of

So well trained, so_ a-ni-

So in-de-ci-sive, so adam-ant. I'm con-tem-
So need your love, so fuck you all. I'm not

-pla-ting, think-ing a-bout think-ing. It's so frust-
scared of dy-ing I just don't want to. If I stopped

-ra-ting, just get a-no-ther drink in. Watch me come un-done.
ly-ing I'd just dis-ap-point you. I come un-done.

They're sell-ing ra-zor blades and mir-rors in the street.

shit.
-mal.

Pray___ that when I'm com - ing down___ you'll be a - sleep.___

If I ev - er hurt___ you your re - venge___ will be___ so sweet, be - cause___ I'm

scum and I'm your___ son.___ I come un - done.___

I come un - done.___

44

So write a - no - ther bal - lad mix it on a Wednes - day.

Sell it on a Thurs - day, buy a yacht by Sat - ur - day, it's a love___ song,___ a

love___ song.___ Do a - no - ther in - ter - view sing a bunch of lies.

Tell a - bout ce - le - bri - ties that I des - pise_ and sing love___ songs._ We sing

love___ songs, so sin - cere.___

so sin - cere.

They're sell - ing ra - zor blades and mir - rors in___ the street.___

CRY ME A RIVER

Words & Music by Justin Timberlake, Scott Storch & Tim Mosley

51

HERE IT COMES AGAIN

Words & Music by Marius De Vries, Melanie Chisholm & Robert Howard

I'M GONNA GETCHA GOOD!

Words & Music by Shania Twain & R.J. Lange

want you for the week-end,   don't want you for a night.   I'm

on-ly in-ter-est-ed   if I can have you for life,___ yeah.   2. I

know I said I'm se-ri-ous,_____ and ba-by I am.

(Verse 3 see block lyric)

You're a fine piece of real es-tate, and I'm gon-na get me some land.___

To Coda

I'm gon - na get-cha if it takes all___ night.___ You can bet-cha by the

time I say___ go, you'll nev - er say___ no.___

D♭   A♭   B♭m

I'm gon - na get-cha, it's a mat-ter of___ fact. I'm gon - na get-cha, don-cha

G♭   D♭   A♭

wor - ry 'bout___ that.___ You can bet your bot-tom dol-lar in___ time, you're gon -

Verse 3:
I've already planned it
Here's how it's gonna be
I'm gonna love you
And you're gonna fall in love with me.

So don't try to run. *etc.*

I CAN'T BREAK DOWN

Words & Music by Pete Glenister, Sinead Quinn & Deni Lew

1. Now I know I can han - dle this,_____ I'll close my

69

IF YOU'RE NOT THE ONE

Words & Music by Daniel Bedingfield

'Cause I miss you, body and soul so strong that it takes my breath away. And I breathe you into my heart and pray for the strength to stand today. 'Cause I love you, whether it's wrong or right and though I can't be with you tonight you know my heart is by your

side. I don't wan-na run a - way_ but I___ can't take it, I___ don't un-der - stand._

___ If I'm not made_ for you_ then why___ does my heart tell___ me that I am?_

___ Is there a-ny way___ that I___ can stay___ in your arms?___

Repeat to fade

Drums

THE LONG GOODBYE

Words & Music by Paul Brady & Ronan Keating

1. I know they say if you love some-bo-dy   you should set them free, (so they
2. Some-times I ask my heart did we_ real-ly   give our love a chance? (Just one

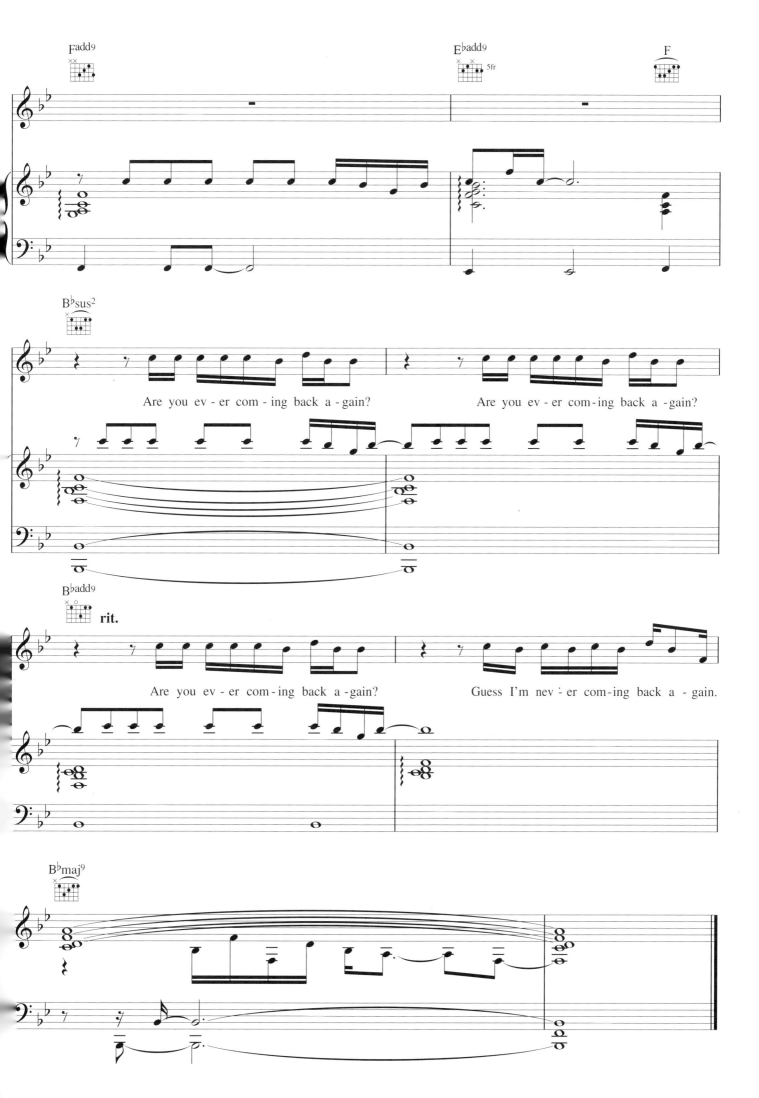

MOVE YOUR FEET

Words & Music by Junior

Don - don - don - don't stop the beat. I ca - can - can - ca - can't con - trol my feet._ Oh, pe - pe -
Sing sing sing sing sing my song and you_____ y - you you you sing a - long._ Just pu -

- pe - peo - ple in the street. Oh, come on_____ ev - 'ry - bo - dy and move_ your feet.
- pu - pu - put_ my re - cord on_____ and all_____ of your trou - bles are dead_ and gone. } Don't

stop. (Don't stop.) Don't stop the beat._ I can't stop. (Can't stop.) Can't stop the beat._ I won't

stop. (Won't stop.) Won't stop the beat_ and go. Ooh._____

RISE & FALL

Words & Music by Craig David, Sting & Dominic Miller

Some-times__ in life__ you feel__ the fight__ is ov-er__ and it seems__ as though the wri-ting's on_____ the wall.__ Su-per-star__ you've fin-ally made it, but once your pic-

-ture be - comes taint - ed it's what they call___ the rise and fall.__

___ Some - times___ in life___ you feel___ the fight___ is ov -
(𝄋) heart.

- er and it seems___ as though the wri - ting's on_____ the

wall.__ Su - per - star___ you've fin - ally made it, but once your pic-

as though the wri-ting's on___ the wall.___ Su - per-star_

___ you've fin-al-ly made it, but once your pic - ture be - comes taint - ed it's what they call

the rise and fall.___ Some - times:

1.

Repeat ad lib.

2.

The rise and fall.___

Some - times___ in life___ you feel___ the fight_ is ov

SHAPE

Words & Music by Sting, Dominic Miller, Craig Dodds, Kenneth Dodds,
Mutya Buena, Kiesha Buchanan, Heidi Range & Siobhan Donaghy

Coda

But that's not the shape of my heart.

That's not the shape, the shape of my heart.

Repeat to fade

SPIRIT IN THE SKY

Words & Music by Norman Greenbaum

1. When I die   and they lay me to rest___   gon-na go___ to the place___
2. Pre-pare your-self, you know it's a must,   got-ta have a friend in Je-
3. Nev-er been a sin-ner,   nev-er sinned.   I got a friend in Je-

best.

Oh,_____ set me up with the spi - rit in the sky._
- ing on up_ to the spi - rit in the sky._

STOLE

Words & Music by Dane Deviller, Sean Hosein & Steve Kipner

good don't get at-ten-tion. One kid with the prom-ise, the bright-est kid in school,_ he's not a
him 'round. Now I wish I would-'ve talked to him, gave him the time of day,_ not turn

fool.
a - way.

Read - ing books a - bout sci - ence, the
If I would - 've then it would - n't have may - be

smart stuff. It's not e - nough, no, 'cause
go this far. He might - 've stayed at home play - ing an - gry

smart don't make you_ cool._ He's not in - vi - si - ble a-
chords on his gui - tar._ He's not in - vi - si - ble a-

109

wait for Sa- tur- day.___ Now we're nev- er gon- na see him slam, fly- in'

high as Ko- be can. His life was stole, oh,___ and now we'll nev- er know.___

To Coda

Vocal ad lib.

(Stole.)

SONGBIRD

Words & Music by Liam Gallagher

1. Talk-ing to the song-bird yes-ter-day,___ flew me to a
(Verse 2 see block lyric, on % instrumental ad lib.)

place not far a-way. She's a lit-tle

Verse 2:
A man can never dream these kinds of things
Especially when she came and spread her wings
Whispered in my ear the things I'd like
Then she flew away into the night.

Gonna write a song etc.

TONIGHT

Words & Music by Steve Mac, Wayne Hector & Jörgen Elofsson

U MAKE ME WANNA

Words & Music by John McLaughlin, Steve Robson & Harry Wilkins

1. To start it off, I know you know me. To come to think of it, it was
2. Well I know that these feel-ings won't end now. They get strong-er if I

on - ly last week that I_____ had a dream__ a - bout us,_____
see you a - gain. Ba - by I'm tired_____ of be -

_____ oh._____
- ing_____ friends._____

That's why I'm here, I'm
I wan - na know if you

writ - ing this song. To tell the truth you know I've been hurt-ing all a - long.
feel the same. And could you tell me do you feel my pain?

make me wan-na fall. You make me wan-na sur-ren-der my soul. I

know this is a feel-ing that I just can't fight. You're the first and last thing

on___ my mind. You make me wan-na love, you make me wan-na fall. You

make me wan-na sur-ren-der my soul. You -der my soul.

PART 2

CONTENTS

ANYONE OF US (STUPID MISTAKE)

Words & Music by Jörgen Elofsson, Per Magnusson & David Kreuger

1. I've been let-ting you down, down. Girl, I know I've been such a fool.

(Verse 2 see block lyric)

Giv-ing in to temp - ta - tion,_ I should-'ve played it cool.

Verse 2:
She was kind of excited
A little crazy, I should of known
She must have altered my senses
'Cause I offered to walk her home.
The situation got out of hand
I hope you understand.

It can happen to any one of us *etc.*

COLOURBLIND

Words & Music by Darius, Pete Glenister & Denny Lew

1. Feel - in' blue ___ when I'm tryin' to for - get the feel - in' that I ___ miss ___ you.

Verse 2:
Feelin' red
When you spend all your time with your friends
And not me instead.
Feelin' black
When I think about all of the things
That I feel I lack.

Feelin' jaded when it's not gone right,
All the colours have faded.
When I feel your eyes, on me
Feeling fine, sublime
When that smile of yours creeps into my mind.
Mm, mm.

CAUGHT IN THE MIDDLE

Words & Music by Ben Adams, Paul Marazzi, Chris Porter & Rick Mitra

1. You said that love___ was just___ a state___ of___

Ev-en though I'm with some-one new,_____ all I can think a-bout_ is you._

(And now_____ I'm caught.)_____ And now I'm caught in the mid-dle.

Things are so dif-f'rent now_ you're gone._____ I thought it'd be ea-sy, I___ was wrong._

And now I'm caught in the mid-dle.

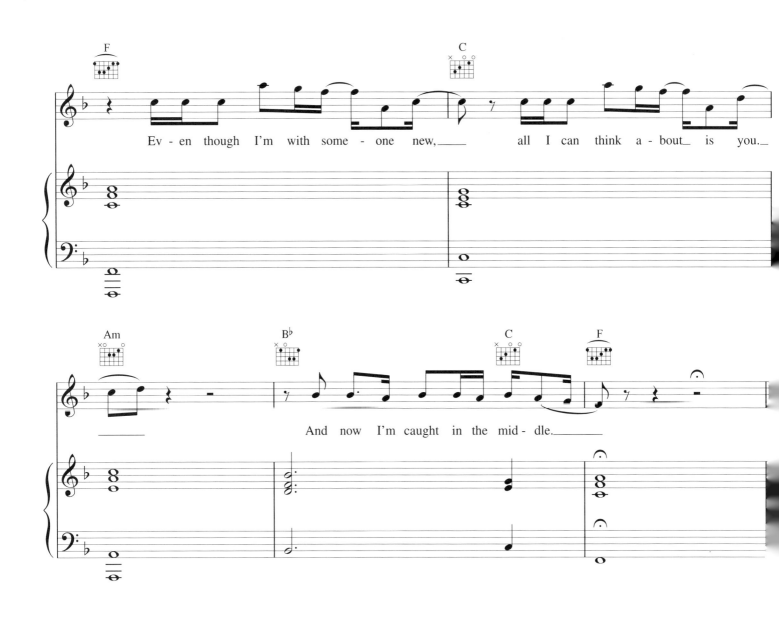

Verse 3:
Moving on, she brings me brighter days
But thoughts of you are in my mind always
Like a memory that I can't erase
It's here to stay

Things are so different *etc.*

EVERGREEN

Words & Music by Jörgen Elofsson, Per Magnusson & David Kreuger

that I need;_ 'cause you're more beau - ti - ful_ than I___ have ev - er seen,_

oh_ yeah._ I'm gon - na take this night and make it ev - er - green._

We can make it last for ev - er more._

Don't_tell_me_that_it feels_like_ love._ I'm gon - na take this

moment___ and make it last for ev - er.³___ I'm gon - na give my heart___

___ a - way___ and pray___ we'll stay___ to - ge - ther. 'Cause you're the one good

rea - son,___ you're the on - ly girl_____ that I need;___ 'cause you're more

beau - ti - ful___ than I___ have ev - er seen.___ I'm gon - na take this

Verse 2:
Touch like an angel
Like velvet to my skin
And I wonder
I wonder why you wanna stay the night
What you're dreaming
What's behind.
Don't tell me, but it feels like love.

I'm gonna take this moment *etc.*

FANTASY

Words & Music by Gareth Young & Andrew Hayman

A-ny game you wan-na play, a-ny-thing you wan-na do. 'Cause you have a-ny-where, a-ny-time, a-ny place.

Show me what to do for you a-ny-thing you want me to.__ I'm bet-ter__ than a-ny-one,

a-ny-one__ you ev-er had. So come on, give up, give in__ to me.__ Show me how I

drive you mad,__ how you wan-na be, be so bad. I ain't fool-in' a-round.
-sy.

Now that you see what's a-bout to go down.___ Now that it's
time, boy to let your-self in.___ You got-ta prove to me boy that you got what it takes. Now I
bet you can't wait for me to be your fan-ta - sy.

Verse 2:
Do you like what you see?
Do you feel that you're closer to reality?
Boy this isn't a dream
Can you be everything that I want you to be?

I'm better than anyone, anyone you ever had
So come on give up, give in to me
Show me how I drive you mad
How you wanna be, be so bad.

I ain't foolin' around *etc.*

FLY BY II

Words & Music by Mikkel SE, Hallgeir Rustan,
Tor Erik Hermansen, Simon Webbe, Randy Alpert & Herb Alpert

1. All dressed up you're good to go,_ check-in' your style from head to toe._ Hooked up and na-tur-al,_
(Verse 2 see block lyric)

you're feel-ing beau-ti-ful._ Nine times out of ten you know,_ late night club like a vi-de-o._ With the

hot stuff, top stuff, yo we got stuff. Oh._ What a night (night)_ so_

far, (far)_ pull-ing up curb-side_ in your car._ (Your_ car)_ What a

sight (sight)__ you__ are,__ (are) think I know some - where__ we can park.__

Af - ter dark. Sys - tem up with the top down and we

got the ci - ty on__ lock - down. Drive - by in the low ride,

hands high when we fly by. Sys - tem up with the top down and we

got the ci - ty on_ lock down.   Drive - by in the low ride,   hands high when we fly by.   (Fly

by.   fly by._ fly by,   fly by.)   fly by.)   Throw your

hands in the air, wave from side   to   side__   let me

see you shake your bo - dy all at the same time.   Throw your   What a

night so____ far, pull - ing up curb - side____ in your car.__

_____ What a sight you are. _____ think I

know some - where_ we can park.____ Af - ter dark._____

Sys - tem up with the top down and we

got the ci - ty on__ lock - down. Drive - by in the low ride,

Verse 2:
Girl it's time to let you know
I'm down if you wanna go
We can take it nice and slow
We got until tomorrow
U.K. style U.K. flow
We got you hot like whoah
With the hot stuff - top stuff - yo, we got stuff.

What a night so far *etc.*

FREAK LIKE ME

Words & Music by Gary Numan, Eugene Hanes, Marc Valentine,
Loren Hill, William Collins, George Clinton & Gary Cooper

1. Let___ me lay___ it on__ the line,___ I got-ta lit-tle

(Verse 2 see block lyrics)

frea-ki-ness___ in-side._____ And you know___ that a man__ has got-ta deal

38

that kind of man 'cause I'm that kind of girl, I've got a

frea-ky sec-ret ev-'ry-bo-dy sing 'cause we don't give a damn a-bout a thing. 'Cause I will be a

freak un-til the day, un-til the dawn. And we can...

(pump) all through the night till the ear-ly morn. Come on and I will

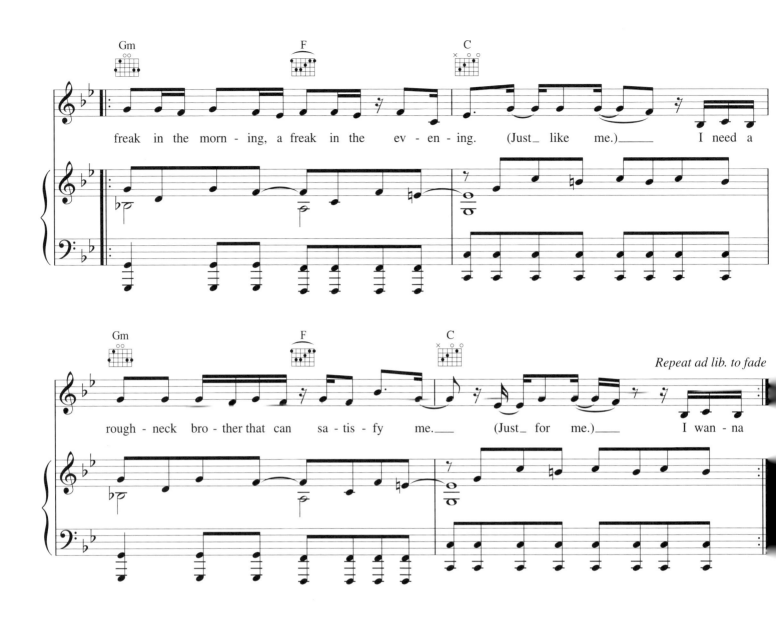

Verse 2:
Boy you're moving kind of slow
You gotta keep it up now there you go
That's just one thing that a man must do
I'm packing all the flavours you need
I got you shook up on your knees
'Cause it's all about the dog in me.

I wanna freak in the morning *etc.*

I'M NOT A GIRL, NOT YET A WOMAN

Words & Music by Max Martin, Rami & Dido

1. I used to think
(Verse 2 see block lyric)

I had the ans-wers to ev-'ry-thing.

But now I know

need is time,— a mo - ment that— is mine,

while I'm in - be - tween.——— 2. I'm not a girl.—

I'm not a girl.————

But if you look at me close - ly you will

Verse 2:
I'm not a girl
There is no need to protect me
It's time that I, learn to face up to this
On my own
I've seen so much more than you know now
So don't tell me to shut my eyes.

I'm not a girl *etc.*

HERO

Words & Music by Enrique Iglesias, Paul Barry & Mark Taylor

Let me be your he - ro.

1. Would you dance if asked you to dance? Would you

run and nev - er look__ back? Would you

49

I can be___ your he - ro ba - by,

I can kiss___ a - way___ the pain,___

I will stand___ by you___ for - ev - er.

You can take my breath a - way.___

2. Would you___

Oh.____ I just wan - na hold   you.__

Verse 2:
Would you swear that you'll always be mine?
Would you lie? Would you run and hide?
Am I in too deep? Have I lost my mind?
I don't care, you're here tonight.

I can be your hero baby *etc.*

IN MY PLACE

Words & Music by Guy Berryman, Jon Buckland, Will Champion & Chris Martin

*Guitar chords capo 2nd fret
*Chord names represent actual sounding chords.
Chord shape represents chord with respect to capo.

1. In my place, in my____ place   were lines that I____could - n't
(Verse 2 see block lyric)

it? Ah, for it? it? Yeah.

Sing - in' please, please, please_

___ come back and sing to me, to me,_ ah me _____ Come on and sing it

Verse 2:
I was scared, I was scared
Tired and under-prepared
But I'll wait for it.
And if you go, if you go
It'll leave me down here on my own
Then I'll wait for you, yeah.

Yeah, how long must you wait *etc.*

JUST A LITTLE

Words & Music by Michelle Escoffery, George Hammond Hagan & John Hammond Hagan

Verse 2:
Let me, I'd do anything if you just let me
Find a way to make you explore
I know you wanna break down those walls, yeah
And it's so challenging
Getting close to you's what I'm imagining
I just wanna see you get down
You gotta let it all out.

Oh baby won't you work it a little *etc.*

KISS KISS

Words & Music by Aksu Sezen, Juliette Jaimes & Steve Welton-Jaimes

Mm!

Mm!

Mm!   1. When you look at me, tell me what you see. This is what you get, it's the way I am.
(Verse 2 see block lyric)

When I look at you I wan -na be, I wan -na be some -where close to hea -ven with Ne -an -der -thal man.

Am   G   Fmaj⁷   G   Am   G

Don't go, I know you wan -na touch me, here, there and ev -'ry -where. Sparks fly when we are to -geth -er,

Fmaj⁷   E⁷   Am   G

you can't de -ny the facts of life._____ You don't have to act like a star,_____ try -ing

Em   Am   G

moves in the back of your car._____ But you know that we can go far,_____ 'cause to-

Verse 2:
You could be mine baby, what's your star sign
Won't you take a step into the lions den
I can hear my conscience calling me, calling me
Say I'm gonna be a bad girl again
Why don't you come on over, we can't leave this all undone
Got a devil on my shoulder, there's no place for you to run.

You don't have to act   *etc.*

LAZY

Words & Music by David Byrne,
Darren Rock, Ashley Beedle & Darren House

_____ comes rush-ing out. No-thing do-in' not or nev-er, how you like me now. Would-

-n't it be mad, would-n't it be fine, la-zy, luck-y la-dy danc-ing, lov-in' all the time.

I'm_____ wick-ed an' I'm la - - zy._____

Oh,_____ don't you wan-na save_____ me?_____

To Coda

la - zy on the job. Got a la - zy mind, a la - zy eye, a la - zy, la - zy Fa - ther.

Hard man,   hard lives,   hard keep - ing it   all   in - side.

Good times,   good god.   I'm so la - zy I al - most stop. (Ha!)

I'm_____   wick - ed an' I'm la - zy.___

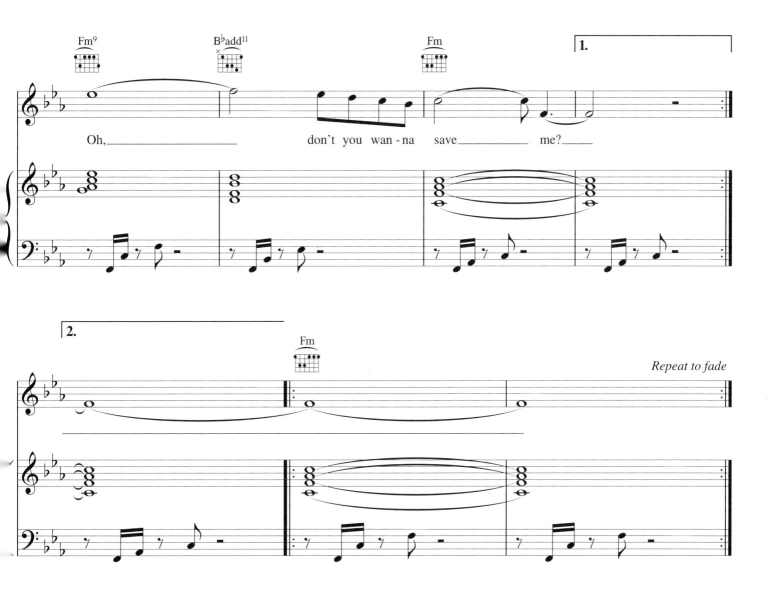

Oh,_____ don't you wan-na save_____ me?_____

Repeat to fade

Verse 2:
Well some folks they got money
And some folks lives are sweet
Some folks make decisions
And some folks clean the streets
Now imagine what it feels like
Imagine how it sounds
Imagine life is perfect
And everything works out
No tears are falling from my eyes
I'm keeping all the pain inside
Now don't you wanna live with me
I'm lazy as a man can be.

I'm wicked and I'm lazy   *etc.*

Verse 3:
Imagine there's a girlfriend
Imagine there's a job
Imagine there's an answer
Imagine there's a God
Imagine I'm a devil
Imagine I'm a saint
Lazy money, lazy sexy, lazy out of space
No tears are falling from my eyes
I'm keeping all the pain inside
Now, don't you wanna live with me
I'm lazy as a man can be.

I'm wicked and I'm lazy   *etc.*

THE LONG AND WINDING ROAD

Words & Music by John Lennon & Paul McCartney

1. The long and wind-ing road____ that
(Verse 2 see block lyric)
leads to your door____ will____ nev-er dis-ap-
-pear, I've seen that road be-fore_____

Verse 2:
The wild and windy night
That the rain washed away
Has left a pool of tears
Crying for the day
Why leave me standing here?
Let me know the way

Many times I've beeen alone *etc.*

A LITTLE LESS CONVERSATION

Words & Music by Billy Strange & Scott Davis

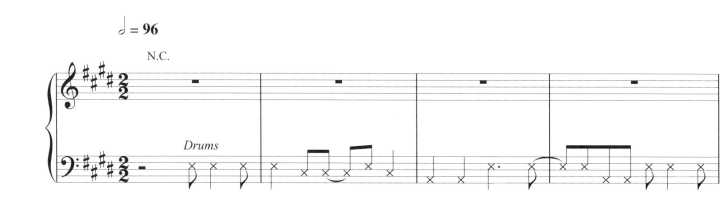

come a-long with me and put your mind at ease.__ Oh, a lit-tle less con-ver-sa-

-tion, a lit-tle more ac-tion, please.

All this ag-gra-va-tion ain't sa-tis-fac-tion-ing me.

A lit-tle more bite, a lit-tle less bark. A

lit-tle less fight and a lit-tle more spark. Close your mouth and op-en up your heart,_ and may-be sa-tis-fy_

_ me.　Sa - tis - fy_ me, ba - by.

Come on ba - by I'm tired of talk - ing.

Grab your coat and let's_ start a - walk - ing.

SOMETHIN' STUPID

Words & Music by C. Carson Parks

know I stand in line un-til you think you have the time to spend an

(Verse 2 see block lyric)

89

The time is right, your per-fume fills my head, the skies get red and oh, the night's so blue. And

Verse 2:
I practise every day to find
Some clever lines to say
To make the meaning come true
But then I think I'll wait until
The evening gets late
And I'm alone with you
The time is right
Your perfume fills my head
The stars get red
And oh, the night's so blue
And then I go and spoil it all
By saying something stupid
Like I love you.

STOP CRYING YOUR HEART OUT

Words & Music by Noel Gallagher

1. Hold___ up,_____ hold___ on,___ don't be scared,_____

you'll nev-er change what's been and__ gone.__ May your smile

(may your smile.)__ Shine__ on__ (shine__ on.)

Don't be scared,__ (don't be scared.)__ Your des-ti-ny__ may

keep you__ warm.__ Cos all of the stars__ are fa-ding a-way,

Cos all of the stars are fa - ding a - way.

Just try not to wor - ry, you'll see them some - day. Just take what you need

and be on your way and stop cry - ing your heart out.

Verse 2:
Get up. Come on
Why you scared?
(I'm not scared)
You'll never change what been and gone.

Cos all of the stars   *etc.*

A THOUSAND MILES

Words & Music by Vanessa Carlton

1. Mak-ing my way down town, walk-ing fast
(Verse 2 see block lyric)

__ fac-es pass,_ and I'm home-bound.

Verse 2:
It's always times like these
When I think of you
And I wonder if you ever think of me
'Cause everything's so wrong
And I don't belong
Living in your precious memory
'Cause I need you
And I miss you
And now I wonder:

If I could fall into the sky *etc.*

WHENEVER, WHEREVER

Words by Shakira & Gloria Estefan
Music by Shakira & Tim Mitchell

1. Luck - y you were born that far a - way so_____ we could both make fun of dis - tance.
(Verse 2 see block lyric)

Verse 2:
Lucky that my lips not only mumble
They spill kisses like a fountain
Lucky that my breasts are small and humble
So you don't confuse them with mountains
Lucky I have strong legs like my mother
To run for cover when I need it
And these two eyes are for no other
The day you leave will cry a river
Le do le le le le, le do le le le le
At your feet, I'm at your feet.

Whenever, wherever *etc.*

WHEREVER YOU WILL GO

Words & Music by Aaron Kamin & Alex Band

Lyrics in score:
1. So late - ly, been won - d'rin, who will be there to take my place.
(Verse 2 see block lyric)

When I'm gone, you'll need love to light the

Verse 2:
And maybe I'll find out a way to make it back some day
To want you, to guide you through the darkest of your days
If a great wave shall fall
It'll fall upon us all
Well then I hope there's someone out there
Who can bring me back to you.

If I could then I would *etc.*

YOUR SONG

Words & Music by Elton John & Bernie Taupin

Mm, if I_____ was a sculp - tor but then a - gain__ no,_____ or a man who makes po - tions in a, a tra - vel - lin' show._____ *Safina* I know it's not__ mu

Elton I know it's not__ mu but it's__ the best__ I___ can do._____

done,_____ I hope you don't mind, I hope you don't mind,_____

that I put__ down in words   rit.   how won-der-ful life is while

you're in__ the world.___ *a tempo*   D.S. al Coda

Kids. And you can tell ev-'ry-bo-dy   this is the

120

2°:
I sat on the roof and I kicked up the moss
Well a few of the verses, they've got me quite cross
But the sun's been quite kind while I wrote this song
It's for people like you that keep it turned on
So excuse me forgetting that these things I do
Just see I've forgotton if they're green or they're blue
Anyway the thing is what I really mean
Oh, yours are the sweetest eyes I've ever seen.

THE TIDE IS HIGH (GET THE FEELING)

Words & Music by John Holt, Howard Barrett, Tyrone Evans, Bill Padley & Jem Godfrey

not the things you do that tease and hurt me_ bad, but it's the way you do the things you
(Verse 4 see block lyrics)

do to me. I'm_ not the kind of girl_ who gives up just_ like

that,_ oh no_woh. 3. The tide is_ high but I'm hold - ing on;

I'm gon - na be your_ num - ber one. The tide is_ high but I'm hold - ing on;

I'm gon-na be your num-ber one. Num - ber one. My num - ber one._

1. Num - - ber one.

2. (Whisper) Number one. one._

5. Ev - 'ry time that I get the feel - ing, you give me some-thing to be-lieve in.

Ev - 'ry time that I got you near me, I know the way that I want it to be._

Verse 4:
Every girl wants you to be her man
But I'll wait right here till it's my turn
I'm not the kind of girl who gives up just like that
Oh no.

Printed by Printwise (Haverhill) Limited, Suffolk 11/06 (602